This book belongs to

_____

To all the teachers I have known and know,
especially the very special teachers in my life:
my husband, my mama, my aunt, my cousins.
You all are the foundation and the pillars of society.
And I thank you and want to honor you!

Designed and illustrated by Ira Baykovska

ISBN: 978-1-7355225-2-4

Andrew Learns about Teachers

part of Andrew's
"Career Day" Book Series

Tiffany Obeng

One Monday in August,
Andrew prepared for his first day of school.
He brushed his teeth, put on his clothes, and
thought to himself, "I look cool."

Andrew grabbed his lunch kit,
picked up his backpack from the floor.
Mama called, "Time to go!"
and they headed out the door.

Mama told Andrew about school
and his teacher, Mr. Lee.

"Mr. Lee? He's my teacher?"
Andrew pondered thoughtfully.

Then Andrew turned and asked,
"Mama, what do teachers do?"

Mama answered,
"Teachers do so much.
Here, I'll tell you."

We learn everything from teachers,
they teach us everything we know.
Teachers encourage us to succeed.
So much to them, we owe.

Teachers teach us

how to count,

how to color,

and how to write.

Teachers teach us

how to read,

how to spell,

and be polite.

Good teachers are also friendly,
good at speaking and listening.

And good teachers are very
patient, respectful and welcoming.

Now, not all teachers are the best,
but when you have the best you'll know.
You'll remember them forever,
even when you're very, very old.

You'll remember what they taught you,
and how they made you feel.
You'll remember that they were special,
and always kept it real.

Andrew gasped, "Teachers do a lot!"
Mama said, "That's not all, you heard?
Teachers do so much more, but now it's time
for school," she urged.

Andrew looked at Mama and asked
if he could one day be a teacher like Mr. Lee?
Mama said to Andrew,
"You sure can!
You can be anything you want to be."

A

LET'S TALK!

YOUR NAME

YOUR GRADE

THE TITLE OF THE BOOK IS

THE AUTHOR IS

THE STORY IS ABOUT

ANDREW'S TEACHER'S NAME IS MR. LEE. WHAT IS THE
NAME OF YOUR TEACHER?

WHAT IS YOUR FAVORITE THING TO LEARN FROM YOUR TEACHER?

DO YOU KNOW OF ANY TEACHERS IN YOUR FAMILY?

DO YOU WANT TO BE A TEACHER ONE DAY?

DO YOU KNOW HARRIETT BALL?!

Harriett Ball was an elementary school teacher and the pioneer educator who inspired the first KIPP charter school. Ms. Ball was known for setting learning to a rhythm. In fact, the name of the school, Knowledge is Power Program, comes from one of Ms. Ball's chants. Ms. Ball trained the co-founders of KIPP by teaching them her original songs, chants and games that she used to encourage learning among her students.

Ms. Ball was born on July 1, 1946 in Rosenberg, Texas. She taught in Austin, Texas and Houston, Texas for 35 years.

CPSIA information can be obtained
at www.ICGtesting.com
Printed in the USA
LVHW071125170421
684247LV00029B/219